T0206582

The Handiest Things

Description

Students explore the idea that a variety of technologies—from chopsticks to calculators—solve problems in our everyday lives. They learn that all technologies have various parts that work together to solve a problem, and then they brainstorm some new parts to improve an invention they use every day—a backpack.

Alignment With the *Next Generation Science Standards*

Performance Expectations

K-2-ETS1-1: Ask questions, make observations, and gather information about a situation people want to change to define a simple problem that can be solved through the development of a new or improved object or tool.

K-2-ETS1-2: Develop a simple sketch, drawing, or physical model to illustrate how the shape of an object helps it function as needed to solve a given problem.

Science and Engineering Practices	Disciplinary Core Ideas	Crosscutting Concept
Asking Questions and Defining Problems Define a simple problem that can be solved through the development of a new or improved object or tool. Constructing Explanations and Designing Solutions Use tools and/or materials to design and/or build a device that solves a specific problem or a solution to a specific problem. Generate and/or compare multiple solutions to a problem.	ETS1.A: Defining and Delimiting Engineering Problems A situation that people want to change or create can be approached as a problem to be solved through engineering. Such problems may have many acceptable solutions. ETS1.B: Developing Possible Solutions Designs can be conveyed through sketches, drawings, or physical models. These representations are useful in communicating ideas for a problem's solutions to other people.	Structure and Function The shape and stability of structures of natural and designed objects are related to their function(s).

Note: The activities in this lesson will help students move toward the performance expectations listed, which is the goal after multiple activities. However, the activities will not by themselves be sufficient to reach the performance expectations.

Contemporary research on how students learn science, reflected in the *Next Generation Science Standards* and other state standards based in *A Framework for K–12 Science Education*, requires that engineering lessons taught as part of the science curriculum provide students opportunities to "acquire and use elements of disciplinary core ideas from physical, life, or Earth and space sciences together with elements of disciplinary core ideas from engineering design to solve design problems." (NGSS Lesson Screener, *www.nextgenscience.org/screener*)

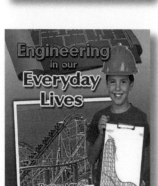

Featured Picture Books

TITLE: *The Handiest Things in the World*
AUTHOR: **Andrew Clements**
PHOTOGRAPHER: **Raquel Jaramillo**
PUBLISHER: **Atheneum Books for Young Readers**
YEAR: **2010**
GENRE: **Non-Narrative Information**
SUMMARY: *Simple rhyme and vivid photographs portray some of the everyday things we use to make life easier, including a dog leash, calculator, watering can, and umbrella. Each photograph on the left-hand page shows a child using his or her hands to do a task, while a photo on the right-hand page shows a "handy" invention completing the same task more efficiently.*

TITLE: *Engineering in Our Everyday Lives*
AUTHOR: **Reagan Miller**
PUBLISHER: **Crabtree Publishing**
YEAR: **2014**
GENRE: **Non-Narrative Information**
SUMMARY: *Simple text and photographs explain that engineers design technologies to solve problems and try to improve existing technologies.*

Time Needed

This lesson will take several class periods. Suggested scheduling is as follows:

Session 1: Engage with The Handiest Things in the World Read-Aloud and Explore with One Handy Thing

Session 2: Explain with Engineering in Our Everyday Lives Read-Aloud and The Handiest Things in the Classroom

Session 3: Elaborate and Evaluate with Build a Better Backpack

Materials

- The Handiest Things Picture Cards (1 precut set per group of 3–4 students)
- 2 umbrellas—1 to demonstrate and 1 to take apart (both for teacher use only)
- Examples of some of the inventions featured in The Handiest Things in the World, such as the following:
    - Chopsticks
    - Dog leash
    - Calculator
    - Butterfly net
    - Watering can

> **SAFETY**
> - Remind students to use caution when working with chopsticks and to keep the chopsticks away from their eyes.
> - Have children wear eye protection if appropriate.

- Broom
- Comb
- Paper fan
- Earmuffs

Student Pages

- One Handy Thing
- Build a Better Backpack
- STEM Everywhere

Background for Teachers

The study of engineering is being emphasized more than ever before in elementary school. In fact, A Framework for K–12 Science Education has included disciplinary core ideas (DCIs) in engineering, technology, and applications of science (ETS) right along with those in life science, Earth and space science, and physical science. In the early grades, students learn that a situation that people want to change or create can be approached as a problem to be solved through engineering, and that engineering problems may have many different solutions. Engineering is sometimes referred to as the "stealth" profession because, although we use countless designed objects each day, we seldom think about the engineering practices involved in the creation and production of these objects. From the pen you write with, to the window you look through, to the cell phone in your pocket, many commonplace objects were designed by engineers.

This lesson not only raises awareness of the work of engineers, but also gives students the opportunity to think like engineers. Students are introduced to the term technology, which is anything made by people that meets a need or solves a problem. Then, they identify various technologies in books and in the classroom. They learn how technologies are made of parts that all work together to solve a problem. By identifying parts and purposes, students begin to learn about the crosscutting concept of structure and function. Students also learn that engineers do not just invent new technologies; they also improve on existing technologies. Finally, students come up with some ways to improve a technology they use every day, a backpack.

Learning Progressions

Below are the DCI grade band endpoints for grades K–2 and 3–5. These are provided to show how student understanding of the DCIs in this lesson will progress in future grade levels.

DCIs	Grades K–2	Grades 3–5
ETS1.A: Defining and Delimiting Engineering Problems	• A situation that people want to change or create can be approached as a problem to be solved through engineering. Such problems may have many acceptable solutions.	• Possible solutions to a problem are limited by available materials and resources (constraints). The success of a designed solution is determined by considering the desired features of a solution (criteria). Different proposals for solutions can be compared on the basis of how well each one meets the specified criteria for success or how well each takes the constraints into account.
ETS1.B: Developing Possible Solutions	• Designs can be conveyed through sketches, drawings, or physical models. These representations are useful in communicating ideas for a problem's solutions to other people.	• Research on a problem should be carried out before beginning to design a solution. Testing a solution involves investigating how well it performs under a range of likely conditions. • Tests are often designed to identify failure points or difficulties, which suggest the elements of the design that need to be improved. • At whatever stage, communicating with peers about proposed solutions is an important part of the design process, and shared ideas can lead to improved designs.

Source: Willard, T., ed. 2015. The NSTA quick-reference guide to the NGSS: Elementary school. Arlington, VA: NSTA Press.

National Science Teaching Association

engage

The Handiest Things in the World Read-Aloud

 Inferring

Show students the cover of The Handiest Things in the World and introduce the author, Andrew Clements, and the photographer, Raquel Jaramillo. Ask

? What do you think this book is about? (Answers will vary.)

Show students the back cover of the book as well as the front and back inside covers. They should notice all the photographs of children's hands and be able to conclude that the book has something to do with hands.

INFERRING

Give each group of three to four students a precut set of the Handiest Things Picture Cards. Tell students that all these items appear in the book and that as you read the book aloud, you would like them to guess which object you are reading about. For each two-page spread, hide the photo as you read the rhyme and have students infer from the rhyme which of the objects the book is describing. When they think they know which one it is, they should hold that card up in the air. After students have guessed, reveal the illustration.

 Synthesizing

After reading, ask

? Why do you think the author titled this book The Handiest Things in the World? (The book features some handy things.)

Next, model how you can find out more information about a book and its author by reading the book jacket. Open to the front jacket flap and read it aloud: "Eight fingers. Two thumbs. Two flat palms. And all those knuckles. But our hands are so much more than that. They were once the first pair of earmuffs, a primitive visor, and a convenient set of chopsticks. The work done by hands centuries and centuries ago paved the way for many of our favorite and most useful tools. The always-clever Andrew Clements reminds us all that the mother of much invention is right at our fingertips."

Then, ask

? Now, why do you think the author decided to call the book The Handiest Things in the World? (Students should realize that all the "handy things" in the book were first done with hands long ago and now they are done with tools.)

Revisit each two-page spread in the book. Show how the child on the left-hand page is using his or her hands to do a task, and the child on the right-hand page is using a tool to do the same task. For each page, discuss how the tool is better than using your hands (e.g., It would be hard to hold your dog with your hands, but a leash makes it easy for you to run and play together. You can't hold much water in your hands, but a watering can will hold a whole lot more.).

explore

One Handy Thing

Show students an umbrella, which is one of the objects featured in The Handiest Things in the World. (In advance, you may want to disassemble another umbrella to more clearly show students the parts.) Ask

? What is an umbrella used for? (to keep you dry in the rain)

OBSERVING AN UMBRELLA

🐛📖 T-Chart

Then, create a T-chart on the board with Part written on the left-hand side and Purpose on the right. Ask

? Look closely at the umbrella. What parts do you see? (handle, fabric, frame, button, strap, etc.)

On the left-hand side of the chart, list the umbrella parts that they observe. It is not important that they know the technical name of each part; a general term will be sufficient for this activity. Then, have students come up with a purpose for each part, and write that purpose on the right-hand side.

Example:

UMBRELLA

Part	Purpose
Handle	To hold it
Frame	To hold the fabric open
Fabric	To block the rain
Button	To open the umbrella
Fastener	To keep the umbrella closed

CCC: Structure and Function
The shape and stability of structures of designed objects are related to their function(s).

After you have filled in the T-chart, ask

? How do all these parts work together to solve one problem? (All the parts serve certain purposes but work together to keep someone from getting wet in the rain.)

Next, give each student the One Handy Thing student page, and give each group of three to four students one of the objects featured in The Handiest Things in the World (or a picture card of the object). Use objects that have multiple parts (e.g., dog leash, calculator, watering can, small broom, baseball cap, comb, earmuffs). On the student page, they will draw a picture of their group's object with the parts labeled and fill out the part and purpose sections of the T-chart. Point out that even something as simple as a comb has parts (handle and teeth) that work together to solve a problem—messy hair. When students are finished, discuss the various parts they labeled and how, just like with the umbrella, all the parts work together to solve a problem.

explain

Engineering in Our Everyday Lives Read-Aloud

 ### Questioning

Ask

? Where did all the handy things from The Handiest Things in the World come from? (a store)

? Where do you think a store gets them? (from a factory)

? Where might a factory get the designs to make them? (Allow them to share their ideas.)

Show students the cover of Engineering in Our Everyday Lives.

 ### Turn and Talk

Have students turn to a partner and discuss their ideas. Ask

? What is engineering? (Answers will vary.)

Tell students that this book will give them more ideas about engineering, and how we rely on it in our everyday lives. Read the book aloud, pausing at pages 6–7, which explain that objects designed by engineers to solve problems are called technologies.

Monitoring Comprehension

After reading those pages, pause to model how good readers monitor their comprehension by verbalizing your "inner conversation." You might say, "Hmm, I thought technology referred to things like computers and cell phones, but now I know it includes other simpler things. Let's read that part again."

After reading page 7, pause to ask students the questions on the inset:

? Which pictures show technologies? (soccer ball, backpack)

? Which pictures show things that are natural? (a bird's nest, lightning)

Continue reading through page 11, pausing to read the questions on the insets and allowing students to answer.

The Handiest Things in the Classroom

After reading page 11, refer to The Handiest Things in the World and explain that all the objects in that book, including the umbrella, are technologies—things that have been designed to solve a problem. Objects that are not designed by humans are called natural objects.

Next, give students a piece of paper, a pencil, and a clipboard. Ask them to walk around the room silently and write or draw a list of as many technolo-

LOOKING FOR TECHNOLOGIES IN OUR CLASSROOM

gies as they can. Give them a few minutes to walk around and make their lists. You may want to play a song while they are making their lists and have them return to their seats when the song is over. Students will quickly realize that almost everything in the room is a technology—from the chair they are sitting in, to pencils they use, to the clothes they are wearing. Have students share some items from their lists. For each technology, discuss what problem it was designed to solve.

Example:

Technology	Problem
Pencil sharpener	Pencil dull or broken
Chair	Legs tired
Desk	Need a place to work and write
Clock	Need to know what time it is
Computer	Need to store and locate data or information

Challenge students to find something that is not a technology, such as a classroom pet, plant, apple, rock, or even themselves! Students will likely notice that the technologies in the classroom greatly outnumber the natural objects.

Next, explain that technologies, such as the umbrella they examined in the explore section of the lesson, are made of parts. Engineers often refer to these parts as structures and the purpose of each part as its function. Refer to the T-chart you made in the explore phase and add the words structure and function above the appropriate columns. Next, have students add the words structure and function to the T-chart on the One Handy Thing student page. You may want to explain that living things also have structures and functions and that they will be exploring that concept in other lessons.

elaborate & evaluate

Build a Better Backpack

Connecting to the Common Core
Reading: Informational Text
KEY IDEAS AND DETAILS: K.1

> **SEP: Asking Questions and Defining Problems**
> Define a simple problem that can be solved through the development of a new or improved object or tool.

 Questioning

Read aloud pages 12–14 in Engineering in Our Everyday Lives. Then, reread the sentences on page 14 that say, "Engineers believe there is always room for improvement! They are always looking for ways to improve the technologies we use." Next, point out the example of the Rain-or-Shine Rider on page 15. Ask

? What structure or part was added to improve the bicycle? (an umbrella)

? What is the function or purpose of that new structure? (keeps you dry in the rain or gives shade in the sunshine)

? How is the Rain-or-Shine Rider better than the original technology (the bicycle)? (You can ride it in any kind of weather.)

Read the section titled "Your Turn!" on page 15 and then tell students that they are going to have the opportunity to improve a technology they probably use every day—their backpacks. Ask

? What problem does a backpack solve? (School supplies are hard to carry; your hands are full.)

? How did people carry things before backpacks? (carried things in their hands, used a duffel bag)

You may want to show students the illustrations from NPR Ed's Tools of the Trade series about the backpack in the article titled "From 'Book Strap' to 'Burrito': A History of the School Backpack" (see "Website" section) for some background and inspiration. Then, give each group of three to four students a backpack to observe. Ask students to examine the backpack, identify as many parts as they can, and discuss each part and its purpose. Students will notice that some backpacks have different parts than others, but all backpacks have some parts in common, such as straps, zippers, pockets, and so on.

Example:

BACKPACK

Structure (Part)	Function (Purpose)
Straps	To hold it on your back
Zipper	To keep things inside and take them out
Mesh side pocket	To hold a water bottle
Small outside zipper pocket	To hold small items

CCC: Structure and Function
The shape and stability of structures of designed objects are related to their function(s).

Word Web

Next, students can brainstorm parts they could add to the backpack to improve it. Make a word web with the target word Backpack in the middle, and organize student ideas in circles that surround the target word. You may want to create categories for their suggestions, such as straps, pockets, bonus features, and so on. Ask guiding questions, such as the following:

? What are some problems you have with your backpack? What parts could you add to solve those problems?

? What part could you add to make it easier to carry?

? Is there something you would like to carry in it that needs a special place? What part could you add to carry it?

? What part or material could you add to make your backpack more fun or stylish?

BUILD A BETTER BACKPACK WORD WEB

 Writing

Give each student a copy of the Build a Better Backpack student page. Tell them that the Better Backpack Company would like them to improve on the company's standard backpack design, which is pictured on the student page. Have students brainstorm about how they would make this backpack better. They can think about what problems they have with their backpacks and how they might solve them, or how to make their backpack more useful or fun. They will give the new and improved backpack a catchy name and draw and label the new structures on the line drawing of the backpack.

> **SEP: Constructing Explanations and Designing Solutions**
> Use tools and/or materials to design a device that solves a specific problem.

When students have completed their designs, explain that engineers have to be good communicators. An important part of an engineer's job is speaking or writing clearly to share ideas with peers and with companies or individuals who will be buying or using the technologies they design. Have students share their better backpack drawings with the class. Ask them to describe the function (purpose) of each new structure (part). Then have them explain why their design is better than the original backpack. After students share their designs, point out that there are multiple solutions to the problem of designing a better backpack!

After the lesson, prompt students to think about their own learning. Ask

? How have your ideas changed about the work of engineers?

? What do you know now about technology that you didn't know before?

? How can you use what you've learned?

? What are you still wondering about engineering?

> **SEP: Constructing Explanations and Designing Solutions**
> Compare multiple solutions to a problem.

A BETTER BACKPACK

STEM Everywhere

Give students the STEM Everywhere student page as a way to involve their families and extend their learning. They can do the activity with an adult helper and share their results with the class.

Opportunities for Differentiated Instruction

This box lists questions and challenges related to the lesson that students may select to research, investigate, or innovate. Students may also use the questions as examples to help them generate their own questions. These questions can help you move your students from the teacher-directed investigation to engaging in the science and engineering practices in a more student-directed format.

Extra Support

For students who are struggling to meet the lesson objectives, provide a question and guide them in the process of collecting research or helping them design procedures or solutions.

Extensions

For students with high interest or who have already met the lesson objectives, have them choose a question (or pose their own question), conduct their own research, and design their own procedures or solutions.

After selecting one of the questions in this box or formulating their own questions, students can individually or collaboratively make predictions, design investigations or surveys to test their predictions, collect evidence, devise explanations, design solutions, or examine related resources. They can communicate their findings through a science notebook, at a poster session or gallery walk, or by producing a media project.

Research

Have students brainstorm researchable questions:

? Who invented the backpack?

? How are backpacks made?

? What are some of the latest improvements to the umbrella?

Investigate

Have students brainstorm testable questions to be solved through science or math:

? Which materials are the best for building a waterproof backpack?

? Which type of thread is the strongest (i.e., can support the most weight) for using in a backpack?

? What is the average weight of the backpacks in our class?

Innovate

Have students brainstorm problems to be solved through engineering:

? How could a pencil be improved?

? How could the classroom pencil sharpener be soundproofed or relocated so that the noise is less distracting?

? How could an umbrella be improved?

Website

"From 'Book Strap' to 'Burrito': A History of the School Backpack"
www.npr.org/sections/ed/2015/11/02/445339503/from-book-strap-to-burrito-a-history-of-the-schoolbackpack

More Books to Read

Beaty, A. 2013. *Rosie Revere, engineer.* New York: Abrams Books for Young Readers..
Summary: Young Rosie dreams of being an engineer. Alone in her room at night, she constructs great inventions from odds and ends. Afraid of failure, Rosie hides her creations under her bed until a fateful visit from her great-great-aunt Rose, who shows her that a first flop isn't something to fear—it's something to celebrate.

Cornwall, G. 2020. *Jabari tries.* Somerville, MA: Candlewick Press.
Summary: A young boy is frustrated as he tries to build a flying machine in his backyard. He learns that perseverance, flexibility, and teamwork can help inventors succeed.

Harper, C. M. 2001. *Imaginative inventions: The who, what, where, when, and why of roller skates, potato chips, marbles, and pie.* New York: Little Brown Books for Young Readers.
Summary: Written in verse and filled with full-color illustrations drawn by the author, this book invites young readers inside the minds of great inventors, encouraging them to think imaginatively as it playfully reveals the origins of inventions such as roller skates, potato chips, eyeglasses, and the vacuum cleaner.

Johnson, R. 2014. *How engineers find solutions.* New York: Crabtree Publishing.
Summary: Part of the *Engineering Up Close* series, this book uses simple text and photographs to describe the kinds of problems engineers solve and outlines the process they use to solve them. Other books in this series include *Engineers Build Models* by Reagan Miller and *Engineers Solve Problems* by Reagan Miller and Crystal Sikkens.

Novak, P. O. 2009. *Engineering the ABCs: How engineers shape our world.* Northville, MI: Ferne Press.
Summary: This engineering ABC book answers questions about how everyday things work and how engineering relates to so many parts of a child's daily life.

Picture Cards

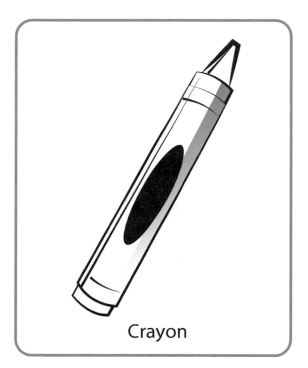

Crayon

Dog leash

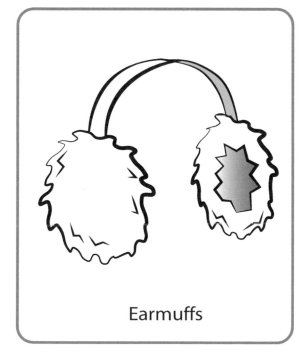

Earmuffs

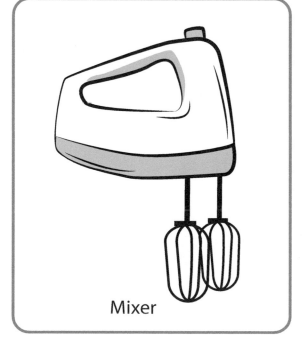

Mixer

Picture Cards

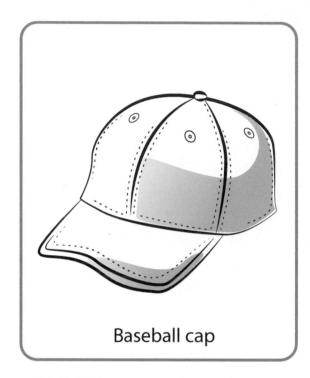

Baseball cap

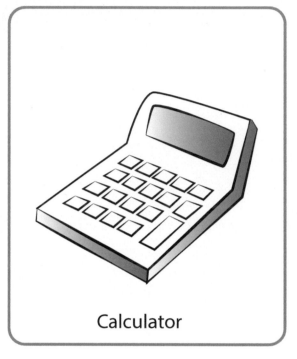

Calculator

Watering can

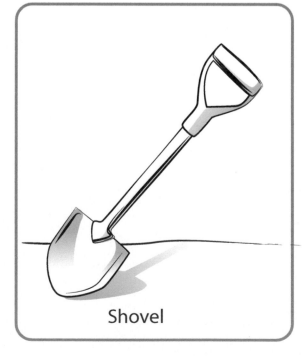

Shovel

National Science Teaching Association

Picture Cards

Broom

Drumsticks

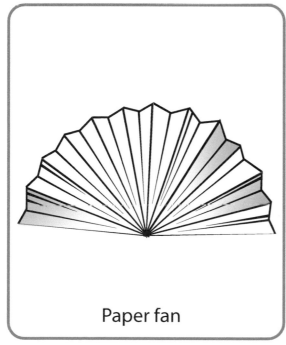

Paper fan

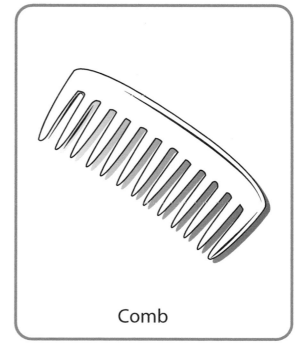

Comb

Picture Cards

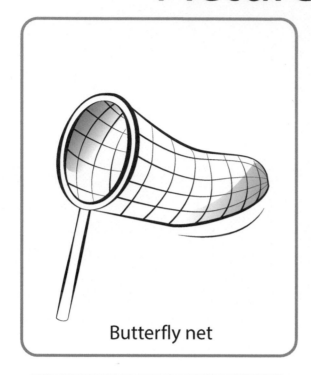

Butterfly net

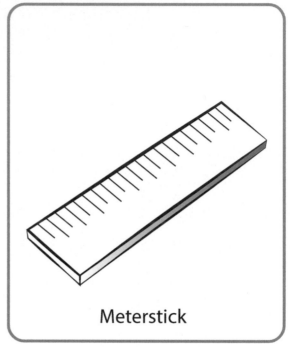

Meterstick

Umbrella

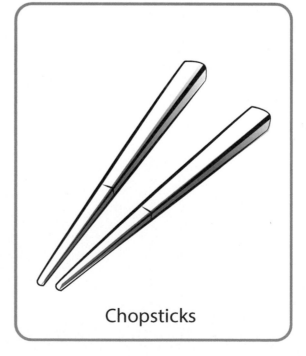

Chopsticks

National Science Teaching Association

Name: _____

One Handy Thing

1. Name of object: _____

2. Labeled sketch of object:

3. What are the object's parts and their purposes?

Part	Purpose

Name: _____

Build a Better Backpack

1. Name of your improved backpack:

   _____

2. Draw and label the new structures on the picture below.

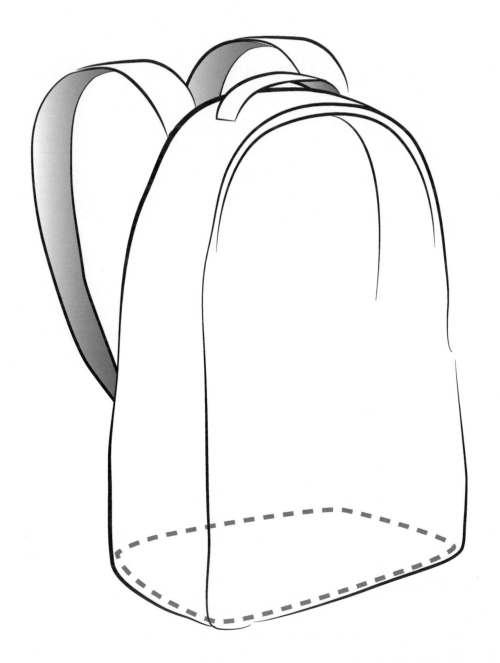

National Science Teaching Association

Name: _____

STEM Everywhere

Dear Families,

At school, we have been learning that **engineers design and improve technologies to solve problems.** A technology can be simple, like a pencil, or complex, like a computer. Like engineers, we designed improvements to a technology we use every day—a backpack! To find out more, ask your learner the following questions and discuss their answers:

• What did you learn?

• What was your favorite part of the lesson?

• What are you still wondering?

At home, improve a simple technology by following these steps together:

1. Choose an everyday object (tool, toy, sports equipment, etc.) that you could improve.

2. Brainstorm ways to make it more useful or more fun.

3. Draw and label a picture of your new-and-improved object.